Managing Editor
Ina Massler Levin, M.A.

Editor-in-Chief
Sharon Coan, M.S. Ed.

Illustrator
Kevin Barnes

Cover Artist
Brenda DiAntonis

Art Coordinator
Kevin Barnes

Imaging
Temo Parra
Rosa C. See

Product Manager
Phil Garcia

Publishers
Rachelle Cracchiolo, M.S. Ed.
Mary Dupuy Smith, M.S. Ed.

Patriotic Puzzlers

Grades 2–5

Authors

Mary Ellen Sterling and Susan Schumann Nowlin

Teacher Created Materials

Teacher Created Materials, Inc.
6421 Industry Way
Westminster, CA 92683
www.teachercreated.com
ISBN-7439-3597-7
©2002 Teacher Created Materials, Inc.
Made in U.S.A.

Table of Contents

Introduction

Patriotic Puzzlers highlights American holidays, symbols, monuments, and ideals through the use of word searches, fill-ins, codes, and crossword puzzles. It provides an imaginative collection of learning activities to teach students about special days and information in American history. Included are reproducible word games for these holidays:

- Dr. Martin Luther King, Jr.'s Birthday
- Abraham Lincoln's Birthday
- George Washington's Birthday
- Memorial Day
- Flag Day

- Fourth of July
- Citizenship Day
- Columbus Day
- Election Day
- Veterans Day

These puzzlers are presented in chronological order and encompass a variety of ability levels for grades 2–5. (It is strongly recommended that the teacher review each page prior to assigning it to the class in order to determine its suitability for group or individual needs.)

An assortment of skills is emphasized throughout the book: reading, vocabulary, math, spelling, and social studies. Solving the puzzles and answering the clues will help students strengthen their reading ability and vocabulary knowledge provide a review of basic math skills, improve spelling skills, and build knowledge of historical facts. These puzzle pages also provide practice in following directions while sparking the imagination.

Throughout the book, the emphasis is on strengthening skills while engaging students in fun and meaningful learning activities.

I Have A Dream

Fill in the puzzle. Use words from the Word List.

Across

1. Dr. Martin Luther _____.
3. He won the _____ Peace Prize.
5. He wanted blacks and whites to be_____.
8. He was born in this month _____.

Down

2. Martin Luther King, Jr., was born in this state.
4. Dr. King told people to not ride on the_____.
6. Dr. King had a _____.
7. He believed blacks and whites were _____.

Word List

friends
dream
January
King
Nobel
Georgia
bus
equal

Martin Luther King, Jr. Crossword

Across

3. The first bus boycott was held in this state.
5. Dr. King won this prize in 1964.
8. "I Have a _____."
11. Dr. King was the pastor of a church in this city.
13. The Civil _____ Bill guaranteed equality for blacks and whites.
14. First name of Dr. King's wife.
15. Dr. King wanted all Americans to be _____.

Down

1. Dr. King and his followers started the _____ Movement.
2. Dr. King was born in this month.
4. Martin Luther King, Jr. was a _____ American.
6. The first boycott was over riding on _____.
7. Dr. Martin Luther _____.
9. Dr. King became a _____.
10. Dr. King was born in this state.
12. To refuse to do something.

Martin Luther King, Jr. Word Search

Find and circle the words from the word list. Words may be across, down, diagonal or backwards.

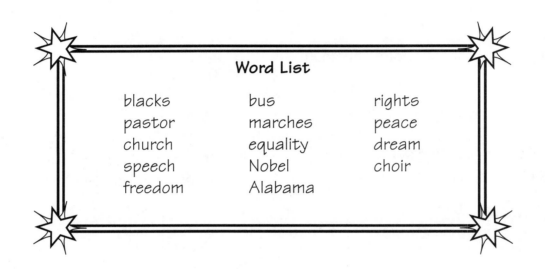

Word List

blacks	bus	rights
pastor	marches	peace
church	equality	dream
speech	Nobel	choir
freedom	Alabama	

O	P	E	C	A	E	P	G	H	J	U	L	K	M	N	B	V	C	F
S	C	N	V	A	W	V	B	S	E	H	C	R	A	M	J	L	K	W
K	L	K	I	U	Y	T	R	E	W	H	B	J	H	C	X	D	S	E
J	S	U	B	G	D	R	E	A	O	L	C	R	O	T	S	A	P	I
K	M	U	E	L	R	N	U	I	S	Y	I	P	I	F	E	N	T	N
C	F	O	R	S	A	E	R	S	P	E	E	C	H	T	C	G	A	E
U	E	N	D	V	B	C	O	I	T	B	V	P	L	H	I	R	B	Z
J	W	Q	N	E	V	D	K	S	D	I	F	A	U	P	L	E	X	D
D	T	O	U	L	E	L	A	S	N	U	C	R	M	I	D	S	Y	P
N	M	O	I	A	L	R	N	G	I	V	C	E	N	A	N	S	E	B
T	H	E	B	E	L	S	F	H	J	H	K	G	H	K	B	N	X	F
R	N	E	B	R	E	I	T	N	P	R	W	N	J	L	J	A	D	C
Q	V	O	N	T	U	Z	T	A	S	T	H	G	I	R	E	T	L	Z
I	N	U	E	M	N	I	B	Y	N	E	M	A	E	R	D	B	F	A

A Great Speech

Write the first letter of each picture to find the title of Martin Luther King, Jr.'s most famous speech.

___ ___ ___ ___ ___

___

___ ___ ___ ___ ___

7

Honest Abe

Word List

lawyer
Civil
South
books
Honest
cabin

Fill in the puzzle. Use words from the WORD LIST.

Across

2. Lincoln loved to read _____.

5. He was a _____.

6. He helped end the _____ War.

Down

1. "_____ Abe" is his nick-name.

3. The North and the _____ fought each other.

4. Lincoln grew up in a log _____.

Abraham Lincoln Crossword Puzzle

Across

2. Lincoln loved to read
_____ .

3. He lived in a _____ cabin.

5. Lincoln was born in this state.

7. Abraham _____ was a great leader.

8. Lincoln's first name.

11. He was a famous _____

12. The Civil War was fought between the North and the _____ .

Down

1. He was called " _____ Abe."

3. He studied to become a _____ .

4. His birthday is in this month.

6. Lincoln was the _____ president.

8. Lincoln's famous speech was the Gettysburg _____ .

9. Lincoln's wife was named _____ .

10. He was president during the _____ War.

Our Sixteenth President

Find and circle the words from the Word List in the puzzle below. Words may be across, down, diagonal or backwards.

H	P	U	L	N	E	B	A	T	S	E	N	O	H	W	P	B	C	X
Y	R	H	O	S	M	N	N	P	C	W	T	F	V	U	K	L	O	P
T	E	I	U	O	U	O	X	I	O	R	E	K	A	E	P	S	R	D
E	S	F	G	U	R	I	V	I	B	G	S	X	V	Y	H	O	L	R
W	I	K	J	T	I	I	K	H	R	A	U	E	P	R	D	B	H	W
T	D	Y	H	H	L	O	R	U	G	X	C	S	C	E	J	K	T	L
U	E	W	A	W	D	E	B	A	T	E	S	G	B	V	L	E	N	T
G	N	I	A	R	S	S	Q	X	K	L	N	M	O	A	Z	P	E	S
X	T	R	Y	K	Y	F	E	C	R	E	Y	W	A	L	Z	S	E	J
K	O	I	N	T	M	Y	V	B	M	E	N	P	A	S	I	S	T	N
K	E	N	T	U	C	K	Y	L	I	O	P	N	C	Z	F	R	X	E
D	E	E	R	F	B	L	H	F	I	I	U	D	C	W	S	A	I	B
R	G	T	Y	H	K	C	O	N	F	E	D	E	R	A	T	E	S	Y
T	O	H	S	I	W	S	U	Z	S	D	F	B	U	V	N	C	O	N

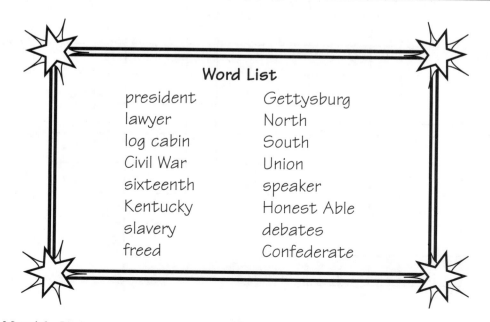

Word List

president	Gettysburg
lawyer	North
log cabin	South
Civil War	Union
sixteenth	speaker
Kentucky	Honest Able
slavery	debates
freed	Confederate

A Presidential Nickname

Answer the math problems. Then place the letter that's next to your answer in the correct blank.

| 8
+7
= S | 4
+7
= O | 9
+1
= A | 2
+10
= E |

| 7
+10
= B | 9
+7
= H | 5
+8
= N | 8
+6
= T |

Abraham Lincoln's nickname was

___ ___ ___ ___ ___ ___   ___ ___ ___
16   11   13   12   15   14   10   17   12

Our First President

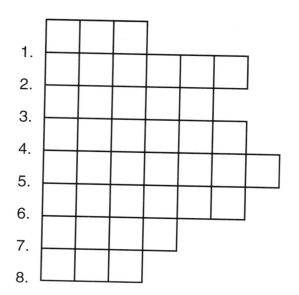

1.
2.
3.
4.
5.
6.
7.
8.

Word List

cherry
lie
army
general
war
first
leader
Martha

Fill in the puzzle. Use words from the word list.

1. "I cannot tell a _____."

2. Washington was a great _____.

3. He was our _____ president.

4. His wife's name was _____.

5. Washington was a _____ in the army.

6. A kind of tree.

7. Washington led the _____.

8. America fought a _____ against England.

Crossing the Delaware

Find and circle the words. The words may be down, across, diagonal or backwards.

W	A	S	H	I	N	G	T	O	N
A	C	R	O	S	S	I	N	G	L
M	O	R	L	P	D	W	P	N	G
A	W	R	I	V	E	R	R	B	T
Y	L	R	D	U	X	C	E	Y	B
R	V	K	A	P	R	O	S	M	I
A	B	A	Y	S	Q	U	I	N	R
U	C	Z	L	O	R	N	D	U	T
R	K	E	S	L	M	T	E	F	H
B	M	Y	E	S	E	R	N	I	D
E	G	R	O	E	G	Y	T	S	A
F	I	R	T	B	L	D	W	G	Y

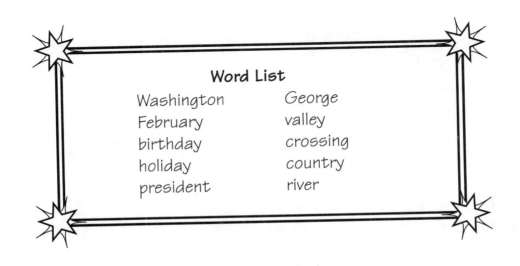

Word List

Washington	George
February	valley
birthday	crossing
holiday	country
president	river

President Washington

Read the story. Find the underlined words in the word search puzzle. Words may be down, across, diagonal or backwards.

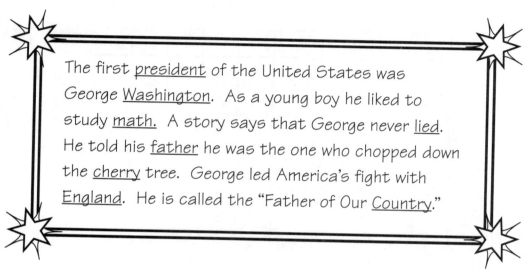

The first <u>president</u> of the United States was George <u>Washington</u>. As a young boy he liked to study <u>math</u>. A story says that George never <u>lied</u>. He told his <u>father</u> he was the one who chopped down the <u>cherry</u> tree. George led America's fight with <u>England</u>. He is called the "Father of Our <u>Country</u>."

I	T	R	E	S	P	Y	R	T	L	U	O	C	F	R	M	O	U	E
F	C	N	V	A	W	V	B	H	J	U	R	M	M	A	T	H	J	N
A	X	Q	E	S	R	F	G	J	L	O	P	N	I	G	E	C	G	G
T	C	I	T	S	I	M	R	A	I	R	A	W	D	L	R	O	W	L
H	D	U	E	Y	R	R	C	H	E	R	R	Y	I	F	E	N	T	A
E	F	O	R	A	O	E	T	S	D	S	N	E	E	T	H	G	A	N
R	S	C	A	D	E	I	O	I	T	R	U	C	E	Z	I	R	E	D
J	W	C	N	C	O	U	N	T	R	Y	R	B	O	O	L	E	S	D
D	T	O	S	L	E	L	S	H	N	U	C	U	E	I	D	S	Y	P
N	M	O	I	O	P	O	R	G	I	V	A	E	N	U	N	S	E	T
T	P	R	E	S	I	D	E	N	T	U	K	G	H	K	M	N	X	F
R	N	E	T	R	E	S	T	H	P	V	C	S	X	M	J	U	D	C
Q	P	L	K	J	H	X	S	D	E	O	B	N	A	B	E	T	C	Z
I	W	A	S	H	I	N	G	T	O	N	J	L	K	T	R	D	A	S

A Title for Our First President

Solve each math problem and write the letter that is next to your answer in the correct spaces below.

25 ÷ 5 = H	4 x9 = S	8 x3 = C	14 ÷ 2 = G	7 x9 = F	45 ÷ 5 = W	12 ÷ 3 = O	30 ÷ 3 = Y
8 x8 = R	5 x6 = A	60 ÷ 10 = T	21 ÷ 7 = E	4 x8 = I	6 x7 = K	3 x6 = U	40 ÷ 5 = N

___ ___ ___ ___ ___ ___   ___ ___ ___ ___ ___ ___ ___ ___ ___ ___
7 3 4 64 7 3   9 30 36 5 32 8 7 6 4 8

___ ___   ___ ___ ___ ___ ___   ___ ___   ___ ___ ___
32 36   42 8 4 9 8   30 36   6 5 3

"___ ___ ___ ___ ___ ___   ___ ___   ___ ___ ___
63 30 6 5 3 64   4 63   4 18 64

___ ___ ___ ___ ___ ___ ___."
24 4 18 8 6 64 10

Parade of Presidents

Fill in the puzzle. Use words from the Word List.

Down

2. The only president to resign from office.
3. He was the first president to speak on the radio.
4. The youngest man to be elected president.
6. The first president to live in the White House.
7. Before he became president, he commanded the Union Army.
10. This president wrote the Gettysburg Address.
12. The only person to become both vice president and president without being elected to those offices.

Across

1. He served the shortest term – one month.
5. "Old Hickory" was his nickname.
8. The oldest man to be elected president.
9. He was sworn into office in an airplane.
11. "The Father of Our Country."
13. He was the second president to be assassinated.

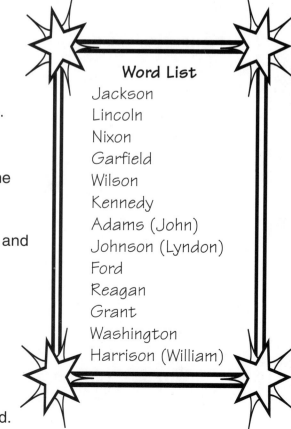

Word List

Jackson
Lincoln
Nixon
Garfield
Wilson
Kennedy
Adams (John)
Johnson (Lyndon)
Ford
Reagan
Grant
Washington
Harrison (William)

A Day to Honor Our Departed Soldiers

Fill in the spaces in the puzzle below with words from the word list. Some clues have been given to help you.

Word List

parade	died
poppies	American
flag	May
flowers	Monday
wars	holiday

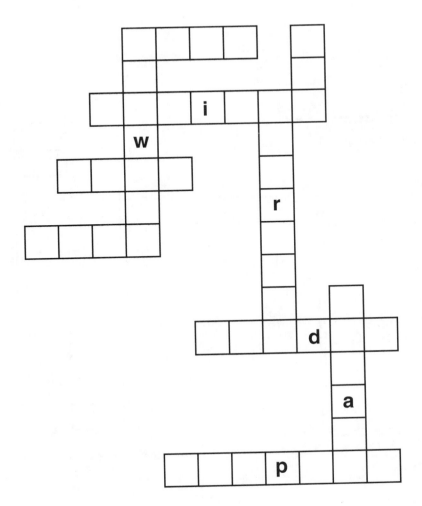

#3597 Patriotic Puzzlers

Memorial Day

Sometmes this holiday is still known as Decoration Day. In 1971 it was declared a national holiday to honor all those who had died in all American wars.

Across

3. Small, red artificial flowers sold on Memorial Day.
7. Another name for Memorial Day: _____ Day.
8. To pay respect.
11. Loyal to one's country.
12. Burial sites.

Down

1. Nation.
2. Someone who served in the armed forces.
4. Marching soldiers, bands, etc.
5. A patriotic holiday celebrated the last Monday of May: _____ Day.
6. The fifth month of the year.
9. A special day of celebration.
10. Poppies, roses, daisies, etc.

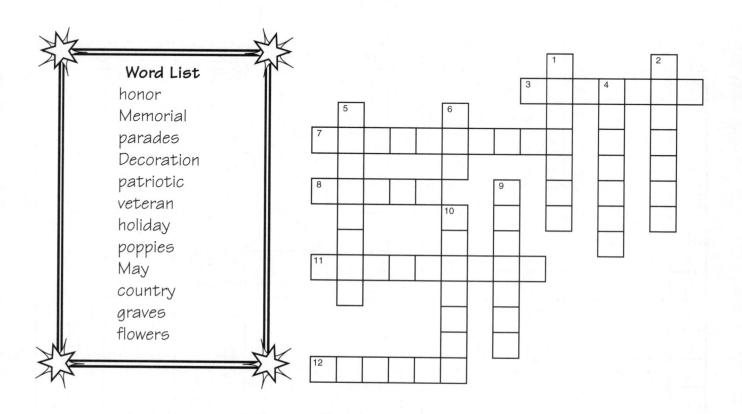

Word List

honor
Memorial
parades
Decoration
patriotic
veteran
holiday
poppies
May
country
graves
flowers

We Celebrate Memorial Day

Read the paragraph below. Find and circle the underlined words in the wordsearch puzzle. Words may be across, down, diagonal, or backwards.

Memorial Day, also known as <u>Decoration</u> Day, is a <u>patriotic</u> <u>holiday</u> in the <u>United States</u>. On the last <u>Monday</u> of <u>May</u>, we honor those <u>Americans</u> who have died in all the wars since the <u>Civil War</u>. People traditionally place <u>flowers</u> and <u>flags</u> on the <u>graves</u> of those who gave their lives for our <u>country</u>. <u>Memorial</u> Day is sometimes called Poppy Day because small, red artificial <u>poppies</u> are sold to help disabled <u>veterans</u>.

H	O	Y	J	N	B	G	F	V	R	A	W	L	I	V	I	C	C	W
O	T	A	J	F	R	W	A	Z	X	C	V	G	H	J	I	O	L	O
L	G	D	N	L	I	U	Y	C	I	T	O	I	R	T	A	P	V	S
I	H	N	C	O	S	P	L	K	J	S	Z	A	R	T	U	N	E	S
D	H	O	E	W	I	N	B	C	O	U	N	T	R	Y	O	T	C	V
A	P	M	T	E	B	T	A	C	I	J	H	B	D	F	A	T	E	E
Y	L	B	S	R	N	O	A	C	R	T	Q	U	L	T	I	O	S	T
A	A	Y	E	S	R	I	V	R	I	U	B	A	S	W	E	Q	X	E
L	I	U	I	D	A	V	I	E	O	R	Y	D	H	B	S	X	J	R
S	R	V	P	G	R	A	V	E	S	C	E	D	A	M	E	M	F	A
G	O	N	P	F	E	X	R	Z	V	T	E	M	M	Y	E	D	L	N
K	M	O	O	T	E	W	X	C	I	O	P	D	A	L	K	E	A	S
T	E	M	P	F	E	S	T	N	V	C	F	S	U	L	P	J	G	S
I	M	Y	U	I	O	P	U	O	J	K	L	F	C	M	A	Y	S	O

A Memorial Day Message

Write the letter that stands for each symbol to complete the message below.

◯ = **A**   ◱ = **H**   ⊕ = **S**

◺ = **C**   ◿ = **I**   ◸ = **T**

▢ = **D**   ⊖ = **L**   ⊠ = **U**

▭ = **E**   ◺ = **N**   ⊠ = **V**

▭ = **F**   ◹ = **O**   ◡ = **W**

◺ = **G**   ◳ = **R**   ◠ = **Y**

On Memorial Day,

for

Our Flag

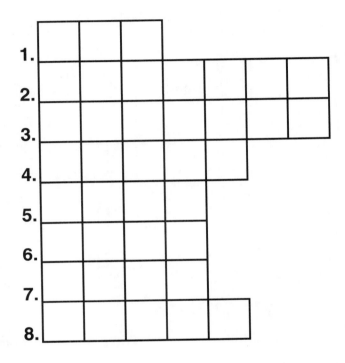

Fill in the puzzle. Use words from the Word List.

1. Some stripes are _____.
2. Everyone loves _____.
3. They are red and white.
4. Some stripes are _____.
5. Our _____ is red, white and blue.
6. Flag Day _____.
7. The stars are on a _____ field.
8. The _____ are white.

Word List
red
white
blue
stars
stripes
June
parades
flag

Hooray for the Flag

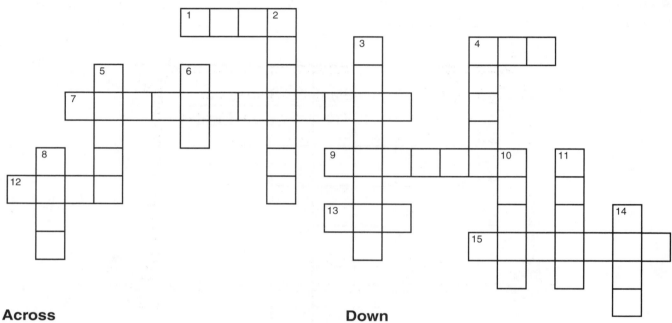

Across

1. Our flag was adopted in this month.

4. Number of white stripes.

7. The flag was adopted in this city.

9. Our flag has thirteen _____ .

12. _____ stands for loyalty.

13. _____ stands for courage.

15. The colonies fought for their

_____ .

Down

2. The colonies won their freedom from

_____ .

3. Number of original colonies.

4. Each colony became a

_____ .

5. _____ stands for purity.

6. The colonists fought in the Revolutionary

_____ .

8. The _____ is the symbol of

our nation.

10. There are fifty _____ on the

flag.

11. Number of red stripes.

14. Betsy _____ may have made

the first flag.

It's A Grand Old Flag

Read the story below. Find all the underlined words in the word search puzzle. Words may be down, across, diagonal, or backwards.

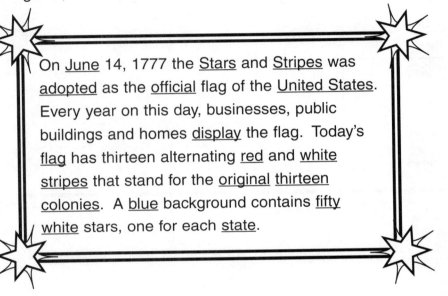

On <u>June</u> 14, 1777 the <u>Stars</u> and <u>Stripes</u> was <u>adopted</u> as the <u>official</u> flag of the <u>United States</u>. Every year on this day, businesses, public buildings and homes <u>display</u> the flag. Today's <u>flag</u> has thirteen alternating <u>red</u> and <u>white</u> <u>stripes</u> that stand for the <u>original</u> <u>thirteen</u> <u>colonies</u>. A <u>blue</u> background contains <u>fifty</u> <u>white</u> stars, one for each <u>state</u>.

D	T	R	E	D	S	R	W	H	I	T	E	R	E	T	A	T	S	F
U	I	T	R	E	W	S	X	C	D	A	F	T	Y	U	I	F	G	S
T	S	S	J	U	N	E	X	L	N	I	D	N	J	T	G	L	C	W
X	B	I	P	D	E	W	S	U	A	O	K	O	I	N	O	A	R	T
J	P	L	J	L	H	Y	T	Y	V	N	Q	R	P	F	E	G	T	N
R	S	V	U	J	A	S	J	T	E	R	I	N	J	T	M	K	L	O
D	E	H	Y	E	T	Y	O	F	Y	T	R	G	X	Z	E	V	E	E
F	I	T	E	A	V	S	Y	I	U	I	V	B	I	P	W	D	B	R
X	N	O	R	T	F	E	U	F	N	U	P	F	M	R	E	L	A	K
P	O	S	I	R	O	P	A	L	A	I	C	I	F	F	O	H	O	X
Q	L	E	C	U	I	I	A	H	J	U	K	I	L	B	L	I	O	Q
I	O	R	T	N	O	R	D	T	H	I	R	T	E	E	N	O	F	X
C	C	O	U	N	I	T	E	D	S	T	A	T	E	S	B	G	F	Z
I	N	J	H	Y	T	S	G	T	Y	H	U	I	L	N	H	G	R	D

Nicknames For the Flag

Write the correct letter of the shape on each line to find two nicknames for the United States flag.

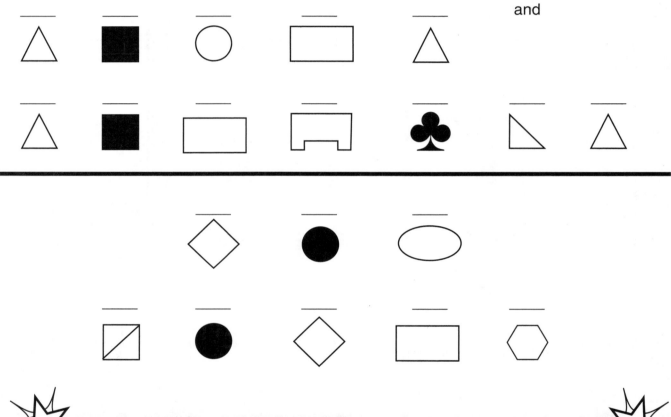

and

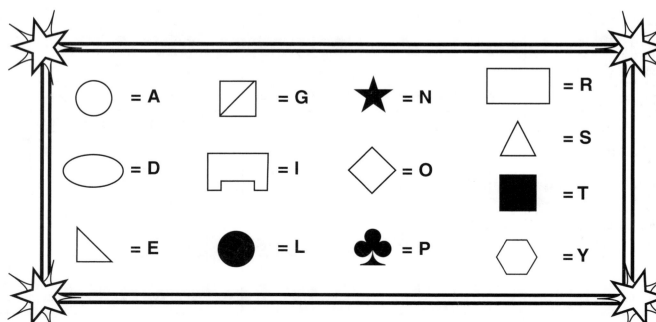

Fourth of July Fun!

Fill in the puzzle. Use words from the Word List.

Word List

picnic
birthday
July
parade
holiday
flag
fireworks

Across

2. These light up the sky.
3. A band marches in this.
5. Happy _____ , America!

Down

1. A special kind of day.
2. This flies on a pole.
3. A special basket for carrying food.
4. This month comes after June.

Happy Birthday, USA!

Across

1. The season between spring and fall.
5. Yankee _____ Dandy.
7. The _____ Bell.
9. One color on our flag.
13. July 4th is our nation's _____.
15. Pack up the _____ basket!
16. A bright display of lights in the sky.
17. _____ Washington.
18. The colonists fought for _____.

Down

2. "_____ Sam" is our nation's symbol.
3. Our nation's birthday is in this month.
4. Another color in our flag.
6. America is the "Land of the _____."
8. A large fire built outside.
10. July 4th is a summer _____.
11. Number of original colonies.
12. The _____ on tea started the Boston Tea Party.
14. Another color in our flag.
15. We often have _____ on July 4th.
16 Our _____ is red, white, and blue.

A Patriotic Holiday

Read the following story. Find the underlined words in the word search puzzle. Words may be down, across, diagonal, or backwards.

The Fourth of July, also known as Independence Day, is the anniversary of the signing of the Declaration of Independence. It is the birthday of our country. Independence Day was first observed in Philadelphia, Pennsylvania in 1776 with a parade and ringing church bells. Today, people celebrate the Fourth of July by having picnics and watching fireworks.

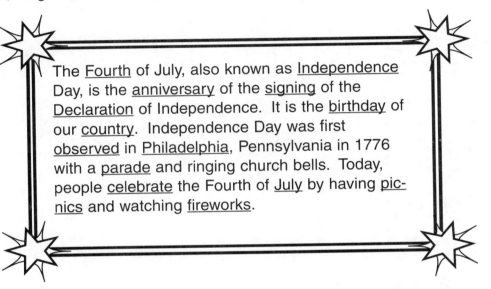

U	Y	A	D	H	T	R	I	B	H	Y	U	I	H	F	U	Y	T	R
P	Y	T	V	G	E	M	T	F	D	C	N	G	I	J	M	I	F	T
H	E	T	A	R	B	E	L	E	C	O	N	R	U	H	N	J	H	S
I	G	N	I	N	G	I	S	K	I	G	E	N	H	D	H	G	R	A
L	N	G	F	C	L	C	S	T	U	W	N	F	E	V	C	S	W	Q
A	G	F	R	T	I	M	A	S	O	G	T	P	J	H	B	X	S	D
D	S	C	P	N	U	R	G	R	F	C	E	P	A	R	A	D	E	E
E	V	F	C	U	A	S	K	N	B	N	R	B	O	P	W	E	S	V
L	B	I	Y	L	F	S	U	H	D	U	H	P	M	Y	E	L	A	R
P	P	O	C	V	G	T	F	E	F	R	T	Y	U	J	L	G	R	E
H	I	E	C	U	A	N	N	I	V	E	R	S	A	R	Y	U	O	S
I	D	R	T	R	E	C	H	U	I	O	L	M	N	B	V	O	J	B
A	D	R	T	G	E	N	B	V	G	F	T	Y	H	U	I	O	L	O
F	O	U	R	T	H	N	J	K	C	O	U	N	T	R	Y	N	G	Q

A Fourth of July Code

Find two ways that people like to celebrate the Fourth of July. Answer each problem below and write the letter for that number in the spaces at the bottom of the page.

$$7 - \overset{P}{\boxed{}} = 3 \qquad\qquad \overset{E}{\boxed{}} + 0 = 10$$

$$2 + \overset{R}{\boxed{}} = 7 \qquad\qquad \overset{D}{\boxed{}} - 2 = 6$$

$$6 - \overset{N}{\boxed{}} = 4 \qquad\qquad 1 + \overset{S}{\boxed{}} = 8$$

$$A + 1 = 10 \qquad\qquad 10 - \overset{C}{\boxed{}} = 4$$
$$\boxed{}$$

$$5 + \overset{I}{\boxed{}} = 8$$

$$\overline{}_{4} \quad \overline{}_{3} \quad \overline{}_{6} \quad \overline{}_{2} \quad \overline{}_{3} \quad \overline{}_{6} \quad \overline{}_{7} \qquad \text{and}$$

$$\overline{}_{4} \quad \overline{}_{9} \quad \overline{}_{5} \quad \overline{}_{9} \quad \overline{}_{8} \quad \overline{}_{10} \quad \overline{}_{7}$$

I Am a Citizen

Fill in the spaces in the puzzle below with words from the Word List. Some clues have been given to help you.

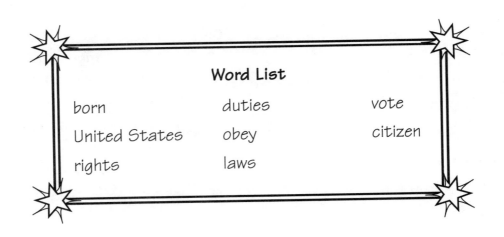

Word List

born	duties	vote
United States	obey	citizen
rights	laws	

Citizenship Is Important

Fill in the puzzle below and learn about citizenship. Use words from the word list.

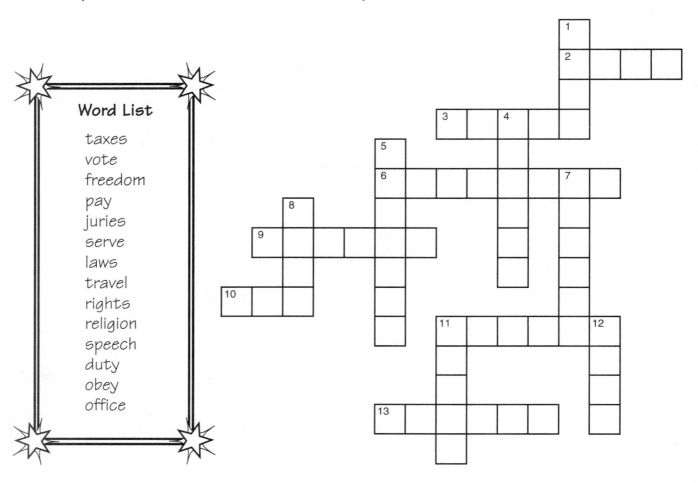

Word List

taxes
vote
freedom
pay
juries
serve
laws
travel
rights
religion
speech
duty
obey
office

Across

2. To follow a command.
3. To wait on; to help.
6. A person's faith.
9. Plural of jury.
10. Wages; _____ check.
11. To go on a journey.
13. A lecture or a talk.

Down

1. To choose someone for an office.
4. Privileges granted by the Constitution.
5. Liberty
7. A position, such as mayor.
8. An obligation.
11. We pay these on your income.
12. Rules we must obey.

Citizenship Day

Read the following paragraph. Find the underlined words in the word search puzzle below. Words may be across, down, diagonal or backwards.

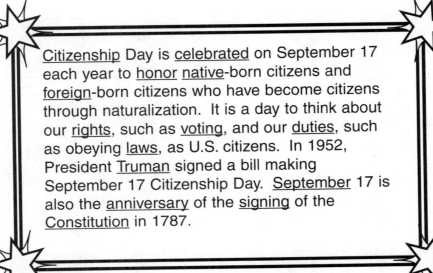

Citizenship Day is <u>celebrated</u> on September 17 each year to <u>honor</u> <u>native</u>-born citizens and <u>foreign</u>-born citizens who have become citizens through naturalization. It is a day to think about our <u>rights</u>, such as <u>voting</u>, and our <u>duties</u>, such as obeying <u>laws</u>, as U.S. citizens. In 1952, President <u>Truman</u> signed a bill making September 17 Citizenship Day. <u>September</u> 17 is also the <u>anniversary</u> of the <u>signing</u> of the <u>Constitution</u> in 1787.

R	I	G	H	T	S	N	H	G	V	F	T	U	I	O	P	P	J	K
Y	F	C	O	N	S	T	I	T	U	T	I	O	N	S	W	H	G	C
R	Y	G	V	C	X	R	E	B	M	E	T	P	E	S	P	O	W	U
A	N	G	I	E	R	O	F	S	D	P	N	N	I	A	O	N	H	V
S	G	F	D	C	X	F	S	D	I	O	J	K	A	V	Y	O	N	T
R	G	C	X	Z	D	I	Y	H	F	G	T	Y	U	M	B	R	P	U
E	V	F	G	T	G	H	S	O	I	U	Y	T	R	E	U	S	E	D
V	H	G	F	N	J	N	G	T	R	E	W	S	D	F	B	R	I	S
I	K	L	I	C	E	L	E	B	R	A	T	E	D	U	H	L	T	E
N	I	N	L	Z	K	G	F	T	Y	U	R	V	O	P	A	T	I	I
N	G	U	I	W	A	T	G	H	V	C	X	I	O	W	U	Y	T	T
A	G	T	J	O	V	O	T	I	N	G	L	T	S	P	O	I	U	U
P	I	Y	U	G	B	H	F	D	S	A	E	A	P	Y	K	N	M	D
C	B	H	J	U	I	O	P	L	B	R	N	N	A	T	R	E	W	T

Good Citizens

Citizens have certain rights and duties. Find out some of these responsibilities by solving the code below. First, answer each problem. Then write the letter that's beside each answer every time you find it in the puzzle below.

14 + 36 = A	61 - 44 = B	23 + 19 = C	85 - 26 = D	35 + 45 = E	52 - 24 = F
16 + 48 = H	72 - 53 = I	47 + 28 = L	50 - 19 = N	34 + 36 = O	81 - 32 = P
15 + 19 = R	43 - 25 = S	18 + 27 = T	84 - 16 = U	28 + 19 = V	50 - 29 = W

28 + 49 = X	72 - 24 = Y

U.S. citizens have the right to

1. ____ ____ ____ ____ and 2. ____ ____ ____ ____
   47   70   45   80   64   70   75   59

____ ____ ____ ____ ____ ____   ____ ____ ____ ____ ____ ____ .
49   68   17   75   19   42   70   28   28   19   42   80

Citizens also have duties such as the duty 1. ____ ____   ____ ____ ____ .
                                              45   70   49   50   48

____ ____ ____ ____ ____   and to 2. ____ ____ ____ ____ ____ ____
45   50   77   80   18   59   80   28   80   31   59

____ ____ ____ ____ ____   ____ ____ ____ ____ ____ ____ ____ .
45   64   80   19   34   42   70   68   31   45   34   48

Land Ho!

Fill in the puzzle. Use words from the word list.

Word List

spices   queen   Spain   boat

small   ocean   land

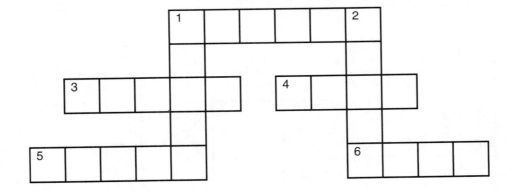

Across

1. Columbus looked for _____

3. The _____ was very big.

4. One _____ was the Santa Maria.

5. The Spanish _____ sent Columbus.

6. He finally saw _____.

Down

1. Columbus sailed from _____.

2. His ship was in size _____.

A Great Adventure

Read the story below. Find the underlined words in the word search puzzle. Words may be down, across, diagonal or backwards.

Christopher Columbus was a famous Italian <u>seaman</u> and <u>navigator</u>. He wanted to find a short sea <u>route</u> to the <u>Indies</u> by sailing east instead of the usual route west. <u>Columbus</u> believed he would find <u>gold</u> there and he also wanted to establish a city for <u>trading</u> products of the East and the West. <u>Queen Isabella</u> of <u>Spain</u> agreed to provide Columbus with money for the voyage's supplies. Three ships, the <u>Niña</u>, the <u>Pinta</u> and the <u>Santa Maria</u> sailed from Palos, Spain in August of 1492. It wasn't until <u>October</u> 12, 1492 that the <u>New World</u>, <u>America</u>, was discovered.

U	E	S	A	N	T	A	M	A	R	I	A	R	D	S	P	O	U	L
K	Y	T	V	G	E	M	T	F	D	C	V	G	H	J	M	S	F	T
Y	E	T	O	S	O	E	X	A	N	I	N	I	U	Y	P	G	R	T
S	R	L	Y	E	S	R	F	H	J	I	K	O	I	A	O	I	H	A
G	D	U	I	A	L	I	N	M	S	Y	I	P	I	F	E	S	T	N
N	F	O	J	M	O	C	T	C	E	S	O	N	J	I	B	N	S	E
I	S	C	P	A	U	A	G	I	I	S	U	R	X	Z	I	V	E	T
D	W	T	E	N	V	G	Y	H	D	E	R	B	O	P	W	E	S	O
A	I	O	Y	T	F	R	U	H	N	U	M	P	M	H	E	L	A	U
R	M	B	I	R	O	T	A	G	I	V	A	N	I	U	N	E	R	R
T	U	E	C	U	I	S	A	H	J	U	K	I	L	B	L	I	O	E
I	N	R	T	R	E	S	D	L	R	O	W	W	E	N	C	O	F	X
Q	V	E	T	E	S	D	C	V	G	H	B	N	P	L	K	C	C	Z
I	Q	U	E	E	N	I	S	A	B	E	L	L	A	T	R	E	A	S

Who Am I?

Write the first letter of each picture below to learn an important fact about a great explorer.

___ ___ ___ ___ ___ ___ ___ ___

___ ___ ___ ___ ___   the

___ ___ ___ ___ ___ ___ ___ ___,

___ ___ ___ ___ ___ ___ ___,   on

___ ___ ___ ___ ___ ___ ___   12, 1492.

Columbus Day Puzzle

Across

1. Columbus was born here.
3. He sailed across the _____ Ocean.
5. The ships left from _____.
6. This king was married to Queen Isabella.
7. Christopher _____ was a sailor and explorer.
9. Ocean _____ could sink ships.
12. Columbus left Spain in this month.
13. Columbus tried to find a route to the _____.
14. One of the three ships.
15. The ships needed _____ to sail.

Down

1. This queen gave Columbus money and ships.
2. One of the three ships.
4. They sighted _____on October 12, 1492.
7. Columbus was the ship's _____.
8. Columbus sailed in the Santa _____ .
9. Synonym for saw.
10. Synonym for sea.
11. The three ships _____ on the ocean.

Election Day

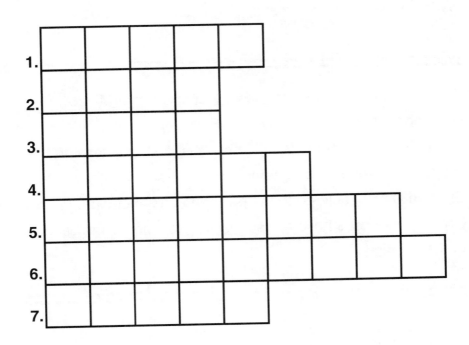

Word List

vote
election
president
booth
speech
free
mayor

Fill in the puzzle. Use words from the word list.

1. This person leads a city _____.

2. Each American has one _____.

3. America is a _____ country.

4. We listen to a _____ .

5. We vote in an _____ .

6. The _____ leads our country.

7. We vote inside a voting _____ .

The Right to Vote

Read the paragraph below to learn about Election Day. Find the underlined words in the word search Puzzle. Words may be across, down, diagonal or backwards.

Election Day is on the first Tuesday after the first Monday in November. On Election Day all U.S. citizens over eighteen years of age have the right to vote. They must first register with the Registrar of Voters and a sample ballot is sent to them. On Election Day, people go to the polls and cast their vote in a voting booth. Americans have a responsibility to vote for the candidates of their choice.

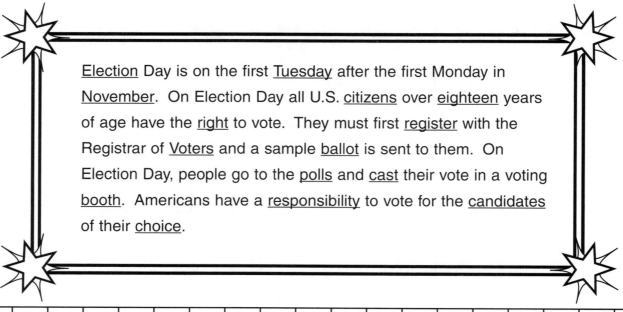

U	E	R	E	S	P	O	N	S	I	B	I	L	I	T	Y	O	U	L
K	Y	C	A	S	T	M	T	F	D	C	V	G	H	J	M	S	F	T
S	E	T	O	S	O	E	X	A	R	E	T	S	I	G	E	R	R	T
E	R	L	C	I	T	I	Z	E	N	S	K	O	I	A	O	I	H	A
T	D	U	I	A	R	I	B	M	S	Y	I	P	I	F	E	S	T	N
A	F	O	J	I	O	C	T	N	E	S	N	E	E	T	H	G	I	E
D	S	C	G	A	E	A	O	I	O	S	U	R	X	Z	I	V	E	Z
I	W	H	E	C	V	V	Y	H	D	I	R	B	O	O	T	H	S	D
D	T	O	I	T	E	R	S	H	N	U	T	U	E	S	D	A	Y	K
N	M	O	I	M	O	T	R	G	I	V	A	C	I	U	N	E	R	P
A	H	E	B	U	I	S	E	H	J	U	K	I	E	B	L	I	O	O
C	N	E	T	R	E	S	T	I	R	O	W	W	E	L	C	O	F	L
Q	R	E	T	E	S	D	O	V	T	O	L	L	A	B	E	C	C	L
I	T	V	E	H	N	I	V	A	B	O	L	A	U	T	R	E	A	S

A Holiday to Remember

Fill in the puzzle about Veterans Day. Use words from the Word List.

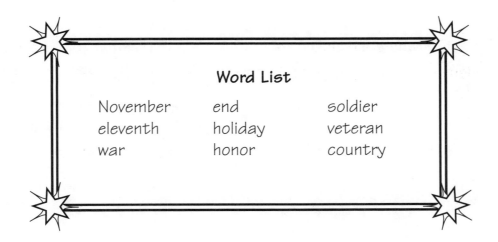

Word List

November	end	soldier
eleventh	holiday	veteran
war	honor	country

Veterans Day

Across

2. Nation
7. A vacation
10. National cemetery where the Unknown Soldier is buried
11. Another name for armistice
12. A warrior

Down

1. Opposite of peace
3. Not known
4. Former members of the armed forces
5. Something that stands for something else
6. To pay respect
8. Our legislature
9. Hidden under the earth

A Day of Remembrance

Read the following paragraph. Find the underlined word in the word search puzzle below. Words may be down, across, diagonal or backwards.

On November 11, 1918 an armistice, or <u>truce</u>, was signed to end <u>World War I</u>. Three years later, <u>Congress</u> declared <u>Armistice</u> Day a <u>holiday</u> to <u>honor</u> those who had served in the war. An unknown <u>soldier</u> was buried in <u>Arlington</u> National Cemetery as a <u>symbol</u> of those who died serving their <u>country</u>. Later, the name was changed to Veterans Day so that the <u>veterans</u> of World War II, the <u>Korean War</u> and now <u>Vietnam</u> would be remembered.

I	T	R	E	S	P	Y	R	T	N	U	O	C	F	R	M	O	U	Y
S	C	N	V	A	W	V	B	H	J	U	R	O	N	O	H	B	A	W
D	X	Q	E	S	R	F	G	J	K	O	P	N	I	G	E	C	G	H
E	A	V	T	S	E	M	S	A	I	R	A	W	D	L	R	O	W	I
T	D	U	E	Y	R	R	I	M	S	Y	I	P	I	F	E	N	T	N
C	F	O	R	A	O	E	T	S	E	S	N	E	E	T	H	G	A	S
D	S	C	A	D	E	I	O	I	T	R	U	C	E	Z	I	R	E	Y
J	W	C	N	I	V	D	Y	H	D	I	R	B	O	O	L	E	S	M
D	T	O	S	L	E	L	S	H	N	U	C	U	E	I	D	S	Y	B
N	M	O	I	O	P	O	R	G	I	V	A	E	N	U	N	S	E	O
T	H	E	B	H	M	S	E	H	J	U	K	G	H	K	M	N	X	L
R	N	E	T	R	E	S	T	V	I	E	T	N	A	M	J	U	D	C
Q	K	O	R	E	A	N	W	A	R	O	B	N	A	B	E	T	C	Z
I	B	U	E	M	N	I	B	A	N	E	J	L	K	T	R	D	A	S

A Veterans Day Code

To learn some facts about Veterans Day, write the letter that comes before the letter that is below each space.

1. Veterans Day used to be called

___ ___ ___ ___ ___ ___ ___ ___ ___ Day.
  B   S   N   J   T   U   J   D   F

2. On Veterans Day we ___ ___ ___ ___ ___ those men and
           I   P   O   P   S

women who served our ___ ___ ___ ___ ___ ___ ___.
             D   P   V   O   U   S   Z

3. Veterans Day is celebrated in ___ ___ ___ ___ ___ ___ ___ ___
                       O   P   W   F   N   C   F   S

with ___ ___ ___ ___ ___ ___ ___ and
     Q   B   S   B   E   F   T

___ ___ ___ ___ ___ ___ ___ ___.
 T   Q   F   F   D   I   F   T

Patriotic Crossword

Use your knowledge of patriotic holidays and symbols to fill in the puzzle below.

Across

3. On July 4, America celebrates its _____ from England.
5. He was our sixteenth president.
7. A symbol of our country.
8. The "Father of our Country."
9. Martin Luther _____, Jr.
10. Also known as Decoration Day.
11. This day honors citizens.

Down

1. Liberty _____.
2. Those who have served in the armed forces.
4. The process of selecting by voting.
6. Christopher _____ is called credited with discovering America.

Answer Key

Page 4 – I Have A Dream

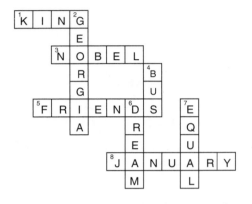

Page 8 – Honest Abe

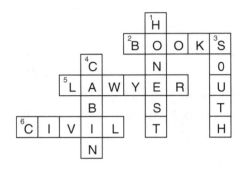

Page 5 – Martin Luther King, Jr. Crossword

Page 9 – Abraham Lincoln Crossword

Page 6 – Martin Luther King, Jr. Wordsearch

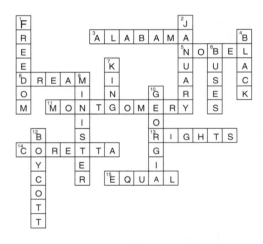

Page 10 – Our Sixteenth President

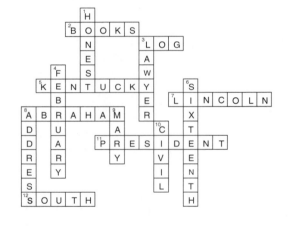

Page 7 – A Great Speech
"I Have a Dream"

Page 11 – A Presidential Nickname
"Honest Abe"

Answer Key *(cont.)*

Page 12 – Our First President

1. lie
2. leader
3. first
4. Martha
5. general
6. cherry
7. army
8. war

Page 13 – Crossing The Delaware

```
W A S H I N G T O N
A C R O S S I N G L
M O R L P D W P N G
A W R I V E R R B T
Y L R D U X C E Y B
R V K A P R O S M I
A B A Y S Q U I N R
U C Z L O R N D U T
R K E S L M T E F H
B M Y E S E R N I D
E G R O E G Y T S A
F I R T B L D W G Y
```

Page 14 – President Washington

```
I T R E S P Y R T L U O C F R M O U E
F C N V A W V B H J U R M M A T H J N
A X Q E S R F G J L O P N I G E C G G
T C I T S I M R A I R A W D L R O W L
H D U E Y R R C H E R R Y I F E N T A
E F O R A O E T S D S N E E T H G A N
J W C N C O U N T R Y R B O O L E S D
D T O S L E L S H N U C U E I D S Y P
N M O I O P O R G I V A E N U N S E T
T P R E S I D E N T U K G H K M N X F
R N E T R E S T H P V C S X M J U D C
Q P L K J H X S D E O B N A B E T C Z
I W A S H I N G T O N J L K T R D A S
```

Page 15 – A Title For Our First President
George Washington is known as the "Father of Our Country."

Page 16 – Parade of Presidents

Page 17 – A Day To Honor Our Departed Soldiers

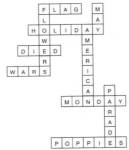

Page 18 – Memorial Day

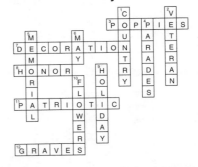

Page 19 – We Celebrate Memorial Day

```
H O Y J N B G F V R A W L I V I C C W
O T A J F R W A Z X C V G H J I O L O
L G D N L I U Y C I T O I R T A P V S
I H N C O S P L K J S Z A R T U N E S
D H O E W I N B C O U N T R Y O T C V
A P M T E B T A C I J H B D F A T E E
Y L B S R N O A C R T Q U L T I O S T
A A Y E S R I V R I U B A S W E Q X E
L I U I D A V I E O R Y D H B S S Y J R
S R V P G R A V E S C E D A M E M F A
G O N P F E X R Z V T E M M Y E D L N
K M O O T E W X C I O P D A L K E A S
T E M P F E S T N V C F S U L P J G S
I M Y U I O P U O J K L F C M A Y S O
```

Answer Key *(cont.)*

Page 20 – A Memorial Day Message

"We honor those who gave their lives for our country."

Page 21 – Our Flag

1. red
2. parades
3. stripes
4. white
5. flag
6. July
7. blue
8. stars

Page 22 – Hooray For The Flag

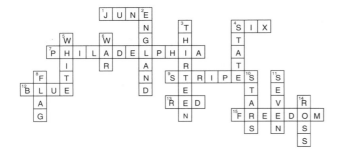

Page 23 – It's A Grand Old Flag

Page 24 – Nicknames For The Flag

Stars and Stripes

Old Glory

Page 25 – Fourth Of July Fun!

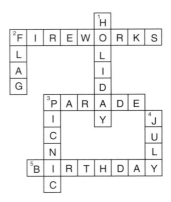

Page 26 – Happy Birthday, USA !

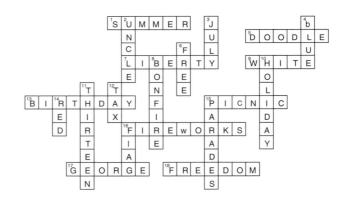

Page 27 – A Patriotic Holiday

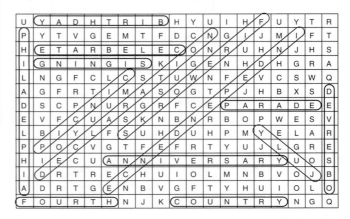

Answer Key *(cont.)*

Page 28 – A Fourth of July Code

"picnics and parades"

Page 29 – I Am a Citizen

Page 30 – Citizenship is Important

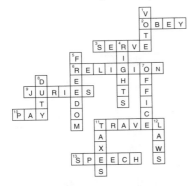

Page 31 – Citizenship Day

Page 32 – Good Citizens

1. Vote
2. Hold public office
1. To Pay Taxes
2. Defend Their Country

Page 33 – Land, Ho!

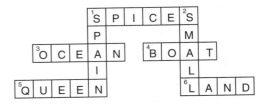

Page 34 – A Great Adventure

Page 35 – Who Am I?

Columbus found the new world, America, on October 12, 1492.

Page 36 – Columbus Day Puzzle

Answer Key *(cont.)*

Page 37 – Election Day

1. Mayor
2. vote
3. free
4. speech
5. election
6. president
7. booth

Page 38 – The Right To Vote

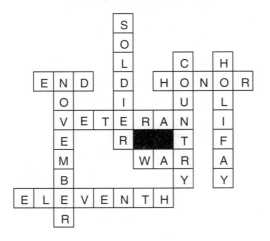

Page 39 – A Holiday To Remember

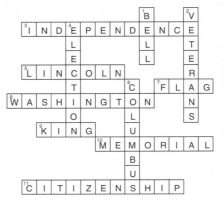

Page 40 – Veterans Day

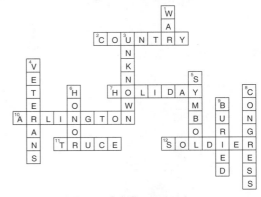

Page 41 – A Day Of Remembrance

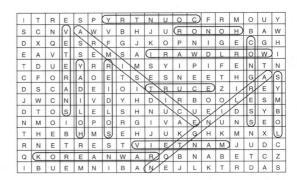

Page 42 – A Veterans Day Code

1. Armistice
2. Honor, Country
3. November, parades, speeches

Page 43 – Patriotic Crossword